# CORAL REEFS

BY THE SAME AUTHORS
*The Science of Life*

# CORAL REEFS

*Written and illustrated by*

LOIS and LOUIS DARLING

THE WORLD PUBLISHING COMPANY

CLEVELAND AND NEW YORK

Published by The World Publishing Company
2231 West 110th Street, Cleveland 2, Ohio

Published simultaneously in Canada by
Nelson, Foster & Scott Ltd.

Library of Congress Catalog Card Number: 63-14780

FIRST EDITION

# *Acknowledgment*

Among many publications we have especially depended upon the following in writing and illustrating *Coral Reefs:* the massive volumes of the *Reports of the Great Barrier Reef Expedition* of 1928–29, Herold J. Wiens' fine review of present-day knowledge in *Atoll Environment and Ecology,* and *Coral Island, Portrait of an Atoll,* by Marston Bates and Donald Abbott. Reports of the work of B. Danielson, F. R. Fosberg, H. S. Ladd, E. P. and H. T. Odum, W. A. Niering, N. D. Newell, and others too numerous to list here, which appeared in the *Atoll Research Bulletin* of the Pacific Science Board's *Scientific Investigations in Micronesia,* have been of untold help. We would like to thank all of the above not only for the use of the results of their work and thought, but for the part they have played in adding to man's store of knowledge of the world about him.

Special thanks are due William A. Niering for answering many questions and for the loan of many publications, and to Mrs. Maurice J. Strauss of the Bingham Oceanographic Laboratory Library for her help with reference material.

LOIS AND LOUIS DARLING

# Contents

# CORAL REEFS

Perhaps you will see a Pacific Ocean coral atoll from a low-flying plane one day. If you do, you will probably remember the sight for the rest of your life. An atoll is one of the most striking and most beautiful forms of that natural phenomenon we call a coral reef.

For hours you may have been flying over the Pacific Ocean, which is so empty that it has been hard to realize that the plane is moving swiftly ahead. It seems instead to hang suspended over the endless sea. But now there is something ahead—a darker blur that is hardly more than an interruption in the long, slow curve of the horizon.

As the plane comes closer, the sight of white surf breaking on a reef gradually emerges from the horizon's mist. The surf-marked reef encloses a calm lagoon. Just within this fragile-looking ring of watery lace, low islets dot the reef here and there on its windward side. The green of their palms and breadfruit and pandanus trees and other plants looks almost gray in contrast with the

7

vivid color of the sea. Inside the islets, on the inner rim
of the reef, golden sands slope into the lagoon. Here the
water loses its deep blue ocean darkness and becomes
brilliant turquoise—a dancing sun-filled green in the
shallows, a deep rich sapphire in the greater depths. On
the largest islet a few roofs show through the trees, a
narrow wharf juts into the shallows of the lagoon, and
canoes that look like small splinters of wood are drawn
up on the near-by beach. A boat moves over the lagoon
waters. With almost a shock you see that those moving
specks by the wharf are people and that they are waving
up at you.

The plane has soon passed over this small atoll, and
ahead there is nothing but the empty ocean again. As
you look back for a last glimpse of this strange ocean

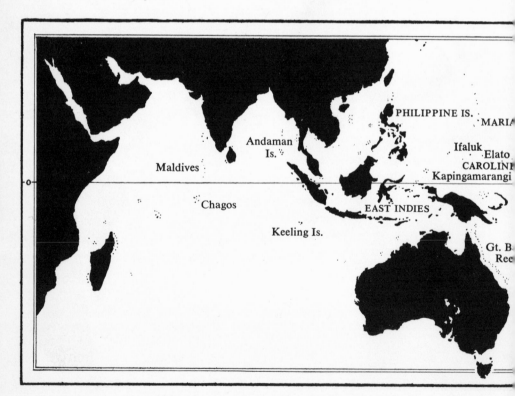

jewel you realize, with a sense of fear, how lonely and small the atoll really is here in the midst of the greatest ocean. The islets' few acres of unsubstantial soil and growing things are only feet above the level of the sea. They seem entirely at the mercy of the constant crash of surf from the mid-Pacific swell or the sudden fury of a hurricane.

There are coral reefs in the Red Sea; around the Philippine Islands; off the northeast coast of Australia; in the East and West Indies; and in the Caribbean; as well as in the vast basins of the Indian and Pacific oceans. Actually the reefs are limited to water warm enough to permit the growth of coral of the reef-building species—about 70° Fahrenheit. Such waters are found mainly between the Tropic of Capricorn, which

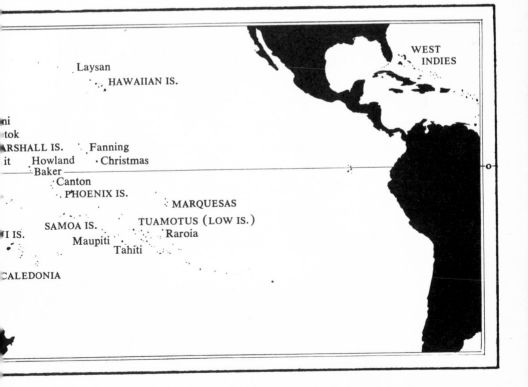

lies 23°27′ south of the equator, and the Tropic of Can-
cer, which lies 23°27′ north of it. But even within these
latitudes coral reefs do not form on the west coasts of
continents where cold currents flow.

On the map the Pacific's atoll clusters do not seem
especially isolated but gathered together in friendly little
bunches. However, the actual distances represented on
the small scale map are tremendous, and the printed
names make the atolls look closer together and more
substantial than they really are. Long, long stretches of
empty sea separate the atolls from other land; many
are hundreds of miles apart within the clusters themselves, and they rise abruptly from dark abysmal depths.

There are three main types of coral reefs: fringing
reefs, barrier reefs, and atolls. A fringing reef is simply
the accumulation of coral stone from the growth of coral
and other animals and plants in the shallow shore waters
surrounding many tropical islands.

Barrier reefs grow farther from the shorelines and rise
steeply from the sea floor in deeper water than do fringing reefs. Between a barrier reef and land, there is a
lagoon channel of comparatively shallow, calm water
protected from the swell of the open sea by the rim of the
reef. Many barrier reefs have coral islets on them. The
Great Barrier Reef of Australia is the largest of this type
in the world, but there are thousands of other barrier
reefs all the way down the scale of size to those like the
one that surrounds the little island of Maupiti in the
South Pacific.

*Barrier reef*

An atoll can be considered a barrier reef which almost completely encircles a high central island, like Maupiti, but without the central island. If the mountainous Maupiti, an extinct volcano, vanished and left only its barrier reef and low coral islets enclosing a shallow lagoon, it would be a perfect atoll. Almost all the atolls in the world are in the Indian and Pacific oceans. It is here also, especially in the vast distances of the South Pacific, that the tales and legends of exploration, adventure, and romance have been born.

*Atoll*

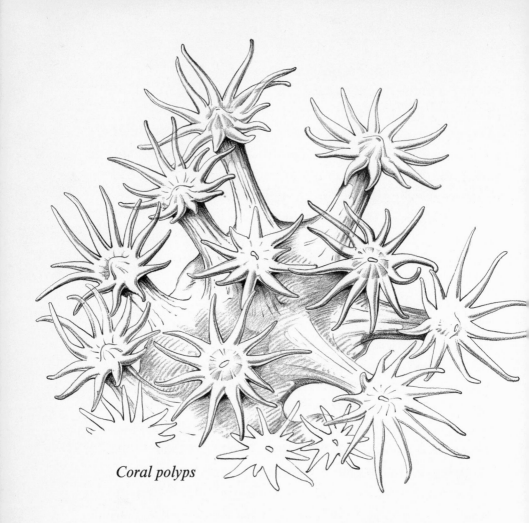

*Coral polyps*

Each flowerlike object in the picture above is not a plant, but an individual animal—a coral polyp of a reef-building species magnified about 20 times. Each small polyp secretes a supporting cup of lime as it grows, a stony skeleton that it leaves behind when it dies. Reef corals are colonial animals. They live together in vast massed colonies. New colonies grow on the stony remains of dead colonies.

The number of coral polyps that now live and that have ever lived is fantastic and beyond any calculation. The results of this living of multitudes, seen in their massed skeletons, are the gigantic underwater mountains, the great blocks and masses and ramparts of solid limestone accumulated over millions of years that we call coral reefs. The coral islands, which project a few feet above the high-tide sea level, are but the smallest part of the reef—comparatively loose collections of coral rubble and thin soil gathered on and about small ledges of coral rock. These islands could not survive, indeed never would have formed at all, if it were not for the living reef between them and the open sea.

Eniwetok Atoll, in the Marshall Islands of the North Pacific, is small as oceanic reefs go. But even it contains 250 cubic miles of limestone submerged beneath the sea, reaching down 4,000 feet to the undersea mount upon which it stands. The Great Barrier Reef of Australia staggers the imagination. It is 1,250 miles long and extends from 7 to 100 miles from the mainland—all the result of the living minute coral creatures and other even simpler forms of life that can extract molecules of calcium from sea water, secrete it in their supporting skeletons, and leave it behind them as deposits of limestone when they die.

There are countless coral reefs: reefs still building and reefs formed long ago. There are dead reefs, reefs raised into mountains, and reefs from long-vanished seas buried deep under what is now dry land. There are reefs elevated high above the level of the sea into lofty islands. There are drowned reefs deep in the sea. There are dead reefs which were formed ages ago with young new reefs growing on top of them, like those found in the West Indies and the Caribbean.

*The buttresses and surge channels of the rim of the reef
break up much of the force of the waves*

For years the great puzzle concerning coral reefs centered mostly about the mystery of the origins of atolls and barrier reefs. It was easy enough to see that a fringing reef in shallow water, given enough time, simply grew up from the ocean floor until the coral reached the surface and could grow no higher. But how could atolls and barrier reefs have risen from the great ocean depths in which they lie? Reef-building coral cannot live below a depth of 180 feet, but at Eniwetok, 10 to 15 miles seaward from the rim of the reef, the water is almost 3 miles deep. Also, what explains the reef-enclosed shallow lagoon feature of atolls?

As in so many branches of natural science, the name Charles Darwin dominates the early study of coral reefs. In 1835, while on his five-year trip around the world as naturalist aboard *HMS Beagle,* he formed the theory concerning the origin of atolls that, with some modern modifications, is still the accepted one.

Actually atolls may still be seen in various stages of formation. We have already given a clue to their origin when we said that if Maupiti's high central volcanic island were to disappear, what was left would then be an atoll. Darwin saw that this is what does happen. Reef-encircled islands often sink slowly beneath the ocean as the sea bottom in the general area subsides. This sort of subsidence happens very slowly, so slowly, in fact, that often coral polyps and other lime-secreting organisms can build up the reef as fast as it sinks. But since most corals thrive best where the surf breaks and ocean water is plentiful, only the enclosing reef builds up rapidly. The coral does not accumulate above the submerged and sinking mountain island. But since the lagoon inside the reef is not exposed to the waves and currents of the open sea, sediment and lagoon-growing corals partly fill it and it remains comparatively shallow.

As is often the case with puzzles, the answer to this one was so beautifully simple that many wondered why they had not thought of it themselves. Darwin writes of the reaction of the great geologist Sir Charles Lyell when he heard of these new ideas: "Lyell, on receiving from the lips of its author a sketch of the new theory, was so overcome with delight that he danced about and threw himself into the wildest contortions, as was his manner when excessively pleased."

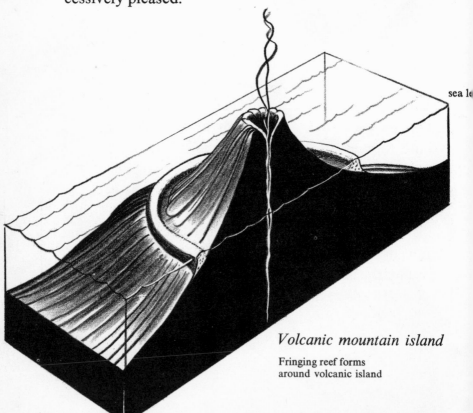

sea le

*Volcanic mountain island*

Fringing reef forms
around volcanic island

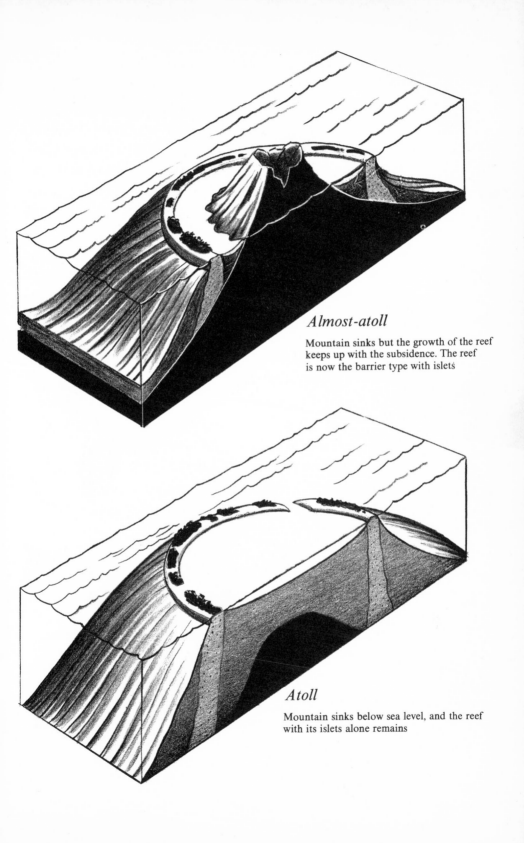

## Almost-atoll

Mountain sinks but the growth of the reef
keeps up with the subsidence. The reef
is now the barrier type with islets

## Atoll

Mountain sinks below sea level, and the reef
with its islets alone remains

However, in the years after Darwin published his findings in his book *Coral Reefs,* much doubt and dissatisfaction arose among some scientists concerning his ideas. The best way to find out if Darwin's theory of reefs was true would have been to drill a hole down through an atoll and actually see, from the make-up of the cores brought up, how thick the coral was. In 1881, toward the end of his life, Darwin wrote in a letter to the famous Harvard professor Louis Agassiz: "I wish some doubly rich millionaire would take it into his head to have borings made in some of the Pacific atolls and bring home cores for slicing from a depth of 500 to 600 feet."

As drilling equipment was crude in those days, 500 to 600 feet seemed very deep. Also the millionaire did not turn up, and national governments did not then spend money freely for scientific research. It was not until this century that modern drilling equipment and public money were able to produce the needed cores. Holes were drilled in several atolls and on the Great Barrier Reef. In every case it was found that the limestone was incredibly thick and not just a coral coating on a reef or sea mountain of some other rock.

The deepest drilling was done at Eniwetok Atoll in 1951. Two holes were made and both showed that the coral stone was over 4,000 feet thick, capping a basalt foundation which was the remains of a long-sunken sea mountain of volcanic origin. Also, the organisms that formed this thick limestone cap all were shallow-water species. At Bikini Atoll, studies with a seismograph

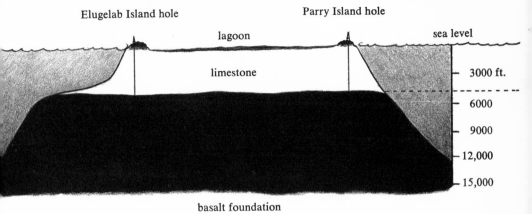

*Cross section showing drill holes at Eniwetok Atoll*

showed that not one volcanic peak but eight make up the atoll's sunken base. How pleased Darwin would have been, and how Lyell would have danced!

Although the cores and other modern discoveries show that the formation of coral reefs is not quite so simple a matter as that we have just described (the eternal forces of erosion, sedimentation, the rise and fall of sea levels, as well as the temporary elevation of some reefs have important effects) they also show that Darwin was essentially right. His brilliant deductive reasoning was all the more remarkable because it was done in South America before Darwin himself had ever seen an atoll!

# THE LIVING REEF

Many books about natural history use the word *living* in their titles: *The Living Forest, The Living Soil, The Living Desert,* and so forth. What these titles, and the title of this part of our book, are saying is not only that the surroundings they are describing are full of living things, but also that these surroundings, or environments, together with all that lives within them—the forest with all its plants and animals, the soil with its minerals and all its organisms, the desert or the reef as a whole—can almost be thought of as single organisms. Actually, each is a close-knit community of living things with its members all dependent upon one another and upon the environment as a whole. Such communities have developed almost as a unit through long ages of evolution. As they developed, the living organisms within them have become adapted to fit the patterns of life of one another and of the particular environment.

A fact common to all such living communities is that plants play the basic part in their existence, whether the

24

community is a coral reef, a forest, the desolate arctic
tundra, or a sun-baked desert. Green plants, powered by
the energy of sunlight, change the lifeless chemicals of
the atmosphere and soil or water into the living material
of their own bodies as they sprout, develop, and grow.
This seemingly miraculous transformation of the non-
living into the living is called photosynthesis (*photo-* is

from a Greek word meaning "light"; *synthesis* is a Greek word meaning "put together"). The process of photosynthesis is really the boundary line between the world of life and that of nonlife. During photosynthesis the energy of the sun used to form the living, or organic, matter of the plants becomes chemically bound into it. Since life is really a matter of using energy to do the work of living, and since *only* green plants can bind this energy into living matter, plants are the absolute base of life itself. They are the producers; all others are consumers. All animals must find their living energy in food that consists of plants, or of animals that have eaten plants, or of animals that have eaten animals that have eaten plants. Even some plants such as fungi and bacteria do not have the power of photosynthesis and are consumers of dead organisms. Of course, man also is bound into such food chains. For instance, we eat fish that have eaten smaller fish that have eaten small animals of the water which subsist upon even smaller aquatic plants. More simply, we eat beef from steers fed with grass and grain or, even more directly, we eat vegetables direct from the sun and soil.

We are all dependent upon plants and could not possibly live without them. But plants have also evolved for millions and millions of years in communities that included animals. Thus plants are also adapted to, affected by, and dependent upon the animals that eat them, fertilize them, use them for shelter, and so on. Thus the interdependence of living things has come to be a two-way affair—a circular pattern that ecologists (the men and

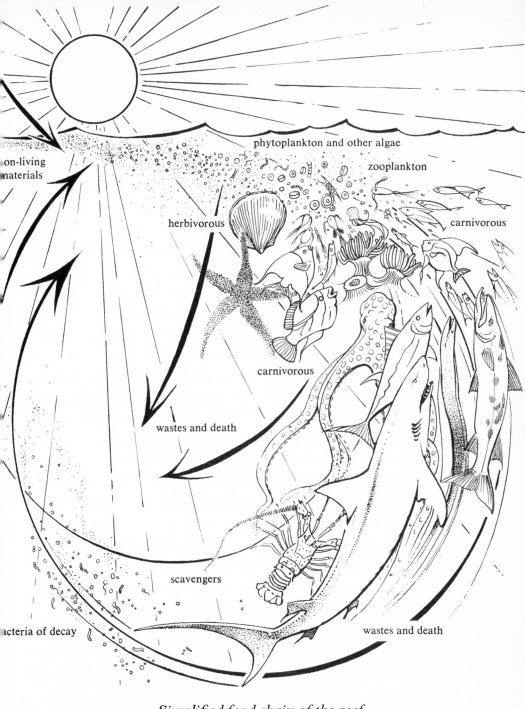

phytoplankton and other algae

zooplankton

non-living materials

herbivorous

carnivorous

carnivorous

wastes and death

scavengers

bacteria of decay

wastes and death

## *Simplified food chain of the reef*

Microscopic plants build their bodies with materials from the atmosphere and in the water by means of the energy of sunlight. The energy, bound in this living vegetable matter, is then available to plant eaters, meat eaters, and finally the bacteria of decay. The materials then return to the water and atmosphere to be used by plants and again pass through this food-energy cycle

women who study these matters) term "food and energy cycles."

You may think that we have strayed a long way from the subject of coral reefs, but the kaleidoscopic community of plants and animals we call the coral reef is as subject to this basic law of nature as is any other. And if we look at it from the ecological point of view, we will have a lot more sense and information than we would if we simply examined its plant and animal members separately as we might the inhabitants of a botanical garden or a zoo.

The important plants of the reef, in fact of almost all watery surroundings, are quite different from most land plants. They have no roots, flowers, or leaves and are simple compared to the plants that do have these special parts, such as the trees, grasses, and herbs most familiar to us. These marine plants are mostly algae. Some, like the diatoms, are very small or even microscopic, while others (some seaweeds, for example) grow up to 200 feet long. Some algae are composed of only a single cell, but many of them are multicellular organisms. None of the algae have the special parts, like roots, leaves, or the systems of tubes or veins through which sap flows, of the more complex plants. However, some algae, like the seaweeds, may have parts with which they attach themselves to rocks or other supports.

Other plants, individually small but large in number and bulk and very important, drift with the tides and currents. These drifting plants as a group have been

given a name based upon two Greek words which de-
scribe them—*phyto-* derived from a word which means
"plant" and *plankton* from a word which means "wandering"—thus *phytoplankton,* the wandering plants. Most
of the phytoplankton are diatoms.

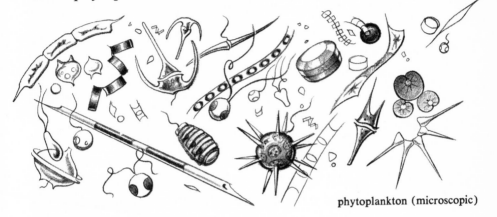

phytoplankton (microscopic)

In spite of being such simple forms of life, the marine
algae can synthesize organic matter just as the more complicated land plants do. Algae existed in the world's
oceans long before there were any land plants at all. So,
just as in dry-land communities, the primary and basic
source of all food energy in the coral-reef community is
plant life.

Among the almost countless forms of animal life, small
and large, that feed directly upon the phytoplankton are
other members of the plankton, the *zooplankton* (*zoo-* is
from a Greek word meaning "animal"). These are the
small and fascinating animals which also drift more or
less helplessly with the ocean currents. The larval forms

zooplankton (enlarged several times)

of shrimps, crabs, lobsters, mollusks, young fishes, and eggs are counted among the zooplankton. Like the phytoplankton, the zooplankton exists in astronomical numbers in the sea. It is a basic food for many other animals, including coral polyps which are thought to be entirely carnivorous, or meat eaters. The zooplankton forms a basic link, a first step in the movement of the energy and materials of life through the food cycles of the coral reef.

While coral is an important builder of coral reefs, it is by no means the only organism that contributes to the stony mass. Another principal builder is a plant which belongs to a group of algae which also manufacture limestone, the calcareous algae. Often these stone-making plants are as important to the reef as the coral itself, sometimes even more so.

The major groups of algae living in the sea are the red, brown, and green algae as well as the diatoms. There are species in each of the first three groups which secrete lime, but one family in the red algae group, Corallinaceae, is the most widespread and plentiful of these calcareous algae. Its members are called, as a group, nullipores. They thrive from the cold waters of the arctic seas, through all the oceans to the Antarctic. You may pick up wave-cast nullipores from beaches all over the world.

The rim of the coral reef, particularly on the side of the prevailing winds, is eternally exposed to the pounding of the surf. The comparatively delicate coral formations cannot easily withstand such a battering. Reefs might not have been able to form and endure at all in the open sea if it were not for one type of nullipore, *Porolithon,* which has a smooth, solid skeleton of limestone. As this plant grows over dead coral colonies, or even smothers live ones, it encrusts the reef where the wear is greatest with a coating of concretelike limestone, cementing the solid coral and coral fragments together into a rather smooth, solid mass. Of course the reef takes its greatest beating where the surf is strongest—on the weather or windward side—and it is in these areas of the most constant and violent surf that *Porolithon* grows best. The glow of its pinkish to reddish coloring adds the enchantment of vivid color to the reef as well as solidity.

one of many species of nullipores (actual size)

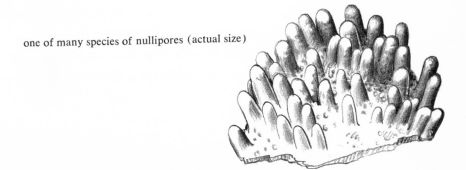

*A West Indian reef*

Plants are of vital and primary importance in the food economy of the coral reef as well as of other communities. But on the reef it is animal life that dominates the "landscape" as trees and other plants do on dry land. The coral and many of its relations grow in numerous and lovely forms and colors, creating not only the "trees" of the reef but its "mountains, caves, hills, and valleys" also.

Coral animals are related to the jellyfish, fresh-water hydras, sea anemones, and other coelenterates (the word means "hollow-gutted"). Coelenterates are among the simplest of those animals whose bodies are made up of more than one cell, the multicellular animals. Coelenterates consist, fundamentally, of just two basic layers of cells: an inside layer which forms the simple hollow of the gut, and an outside layer or "skin." This simple animal is saclike; its gut is open at one end only. Food is taken from the water into the opening, digestion takes place in the gut, and waste products are ejected back into the water through the single opening. This "mouth" is usually encircled by tentacles equipped with paralyzing-poison stinging darts which can kill or numb small prey, and entangling threads which can ensnare it while the tentacles draw it into the mouth.

The fresh-water hydra shows the organization of the coelenterate in what is perhaps its simplest form. The hydra's cousins, the sea anemones, jellyfish, and corals are a bit more complex because of special parts, but they are basically the same in their fundamental workings.

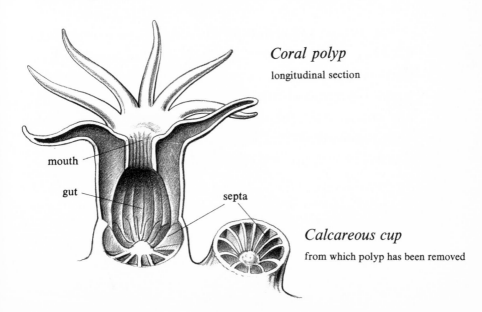

mouth

gut

septa

*Coral polyp*
longitudinal section

*Calcareous cup*
from which polyp has been removed

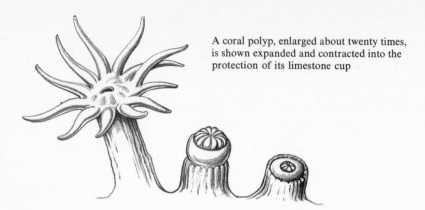

A coral polyp, enlarged about twenty times, is shown expanded and contracted into the protection of its limestone cup

There are many different kinds of corals found in many different parts of the world's seas. Some even live at great depths in cold northern waters. The familiar pink coral used for jewelry is not concerned with coral reefs at all and is found mostly in Japanese and Mediterranean waters. Although some corals do not secrete limestone skeletons, all of the reef-building species do, and all of the reef species live together in huge colonies totaling innumerable animals.

The reef corals reproduce in two ways: One is sexual, the usual way in the world of life—the eggs of one individual are fertilized by sperm from another. New coral colonies originate in this way. However, unlike most animals we are familiar with, each individual coral polyp produces both eggs and sperm; there are no male and female corals. But both the eggs and sperm do not often ripen at the same time in the same polyp, so that a polyp does not fertilize itself. Coral eggs usually become fertilized when sperm which has been released into the water by one polyp drifts into the body of another whose eggs are ripe and ready for fertilization. The eggs then develop, hatch, and the new coral larvae reach the water by way of the parent polyp's "mouth." The larvae may then drift in the ocean for days or weeks until they reach a place to settle that furnishes the proper conditions for growth. Of course, far more are lost in the open sea than survive. But corals reproduce in such unimaginable numbers that equally unimaginable billions of them do survive to start new coral colonies.

When the new coral, alone or several together, settles on some favorable support in water that provides the proper light, food, and oxygen, it secretes its limy supporting base and begins to live as an adult. It then begins to reproduce itself by the second method: budding. New polyps, exactly like the parent, bud from it. These new polyps produce buds in turn as they mature and their

*Budding*

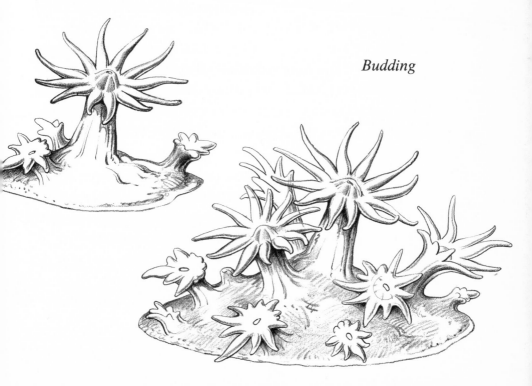

buds grow up and bud. On many coelenterates these buds break off when they are fully developed to drift away and start life for themselves. But in the colonial corals these new individuals remain attached to and are part of the colony. The colonial way of life comes about because of this method of reproduction. It does not take long for huge colonies to form that may reach as much as ten feet in diameter. As the colonies grow, the outermost and uppermost polyps do most of the feeding while the corals in the inner and lower parts die and leave only the limestone skeleton. When whole colonies die new generations of larvae settle on the firm skeleton support and add new layers of stone.

It is hard to determine the speed of the growth of coral as it varies tremendously from place to place. It has been estimated that the average rate may be over a yard in 40 years. Some reefs may be growing upward at a rate of well over two yards each century, which is very fast when you reflect that we are now thinking in terms of hundreds of centuries rather than days, months, or years. There are cases of very rapid growth, probably only under absolutely ideal conditions. A channel in a coral reef in the Andaman Islands had a depth of 36 feet in 1887. In 1924 the same channel had a depth of about one foot.

In spite of the fact that each polyp of a colonial coral remains physically connected to every other polyp, each is an individual, carnivorous animal, eating, taking in oxygen from ocean water, and reproducing itself both sexually and by budding.

A curious and puzzling problem about reef corals is that there seems to be more coral in a reef than there is zooplankton in the water to feed it. Coral polyps are ordinarily thought of as carnivorous animals. But certain algae live in the tissue of the coral. While these algae are separate plant organisms and have no relationship whatever to the coral except that they live in them, they are found nowhere else. Like any other green plants, the algae are capable of photosynthesis and of producing their own materials of life, but instead of obtaining raw materials from the water, they obtain them from the coral in the form of carbon dioxide and nitrogenous wastes—byproducts of animal life processes (metabolism). This situation is called *symbiosis,* which means the living together very closely of two dissimilar organisms, usually to the advantage of one or both and harmful to neither.

While this association of coral and algae is clearly advantageous to the algae, whether or not it is helpful to the coral is not clear. Some investigators have found that coral can grow perfectly well without its algae. However, this can only be done under experimental conditions and so proves little about the natural relationship on the reef.

Others claim that the algae is of decided benefit to the coral and that the combination is an almost completely balanced plant and animal community within itself. The algae provide plant food and oxygen for the coral, and the coral provides plant nutrients and carbon dioxide for the algae.

The sun, of course, as in other plant and animal communities, powers the whole system by furnishing the energy used by the algae to manufacture the plant food. The only other material coming into the system is through the coral's consumption of zooplankton at night when the algae are not photosynthesizing. The oxygen produced as a byproduct of photosynthesis appears to be of definite value as a supplement to the dissolved oxygen in the water that reaches each polyp in the dense coral colonies.

Many other forms of life also contribute to the mass of the reef. Echinoderms—starfish, sea urchins, and their relatives—leave limy skeletons behind. Many mollusks, from small snails no bigger than pinheads through an amazing variety of form and size to the giant clam *Tridacna deresa* (which may weigh from 200 to 300 pounds) become part of the reef when they die. Even the minute single-celled Foraminifera manufacture limy

shells and exist in such astronomical numbers that their discarded shells make up an important part of the "coral" sand of the atolls. Their shells also fill up cracks and chinks and crevices in coral reefs. A "foram," as it is affectionately called, is often no bigger than the size of a period on this page and yet many are more intricate and more beautiful than the most elaborate jeweled crowns of emperors.

One of the reasons that the life of a coral reef is so varied is that it offers to both plants and animals innumerable opportunities for different ways of living. The rim area with its boiling surf and caverned surge channels; the deeper, quieter water of the ocean face of the reef as it descends into abysmal depths; the shallow calmer water behind the reef's rim broken by deeper pools; the lagoon's shoals and depths, dark caverns and grottoes and coral knolls; the sandy beaches of the reef's islands, lagoon mud flats, and watery flats of turtle grass—all these different surroundings and more are occupied by a fantastic variety of living things with a range of adaptations which provide unimaginable opportunities for living. This prodigy of life leads to a phantasmagoria of form and color and activity that leaves one mentally gasping and is unequaled anywhere else in the world.

The reef fishes may best typify this wonderland. The small gaily colored fishes seem more like troops of bright butterflies or companies of jungle birds than like the austere gray or silver fish we know best. Many of them are queerly shaped and have entrancing names which emphasize their endless variety: polkadot wrasses, fantail filefish, longnose butterfly fish, damselfish, squirrelfish, angelfish, razor fish, triggerfish, lionfish, sailfin and convict tangs, scorpion fish, goatfish, birdfish, parrot fish,

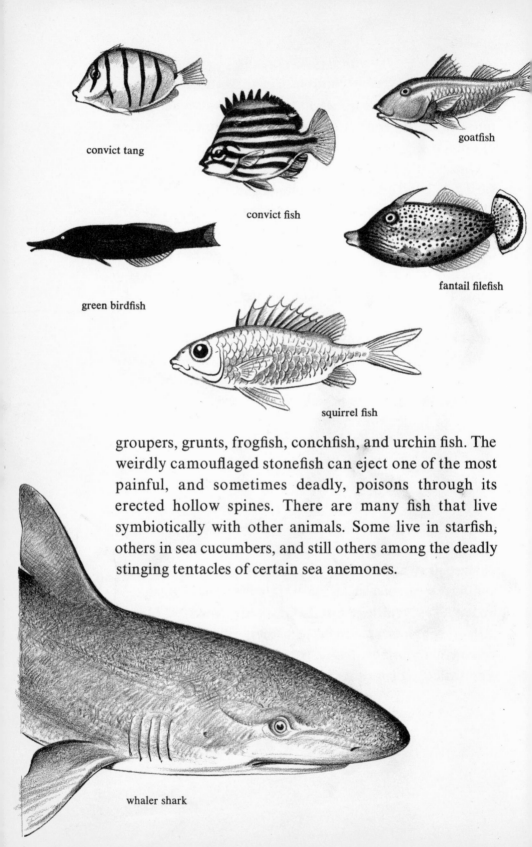

convict tang

convict fish

goatfish

fantail filefish

green birdfish

squirrel fish

groupers, grunts, frogfish, conchfish, and urchin fish. The weirdly camouflaged stonefish can eject one of the most painful, and sometimes deadly, poisons through its erected hollow spines. There are many fish that live symbiotically with other animals. Some live in starfish, others in sea cucumbers, and still others among the deadly stinging tentacles of certain sea anemones.

whaler shark

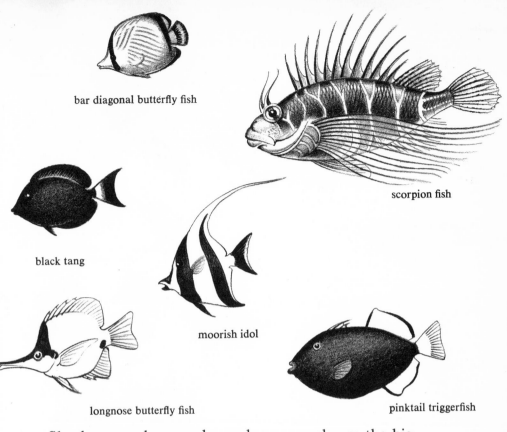

bar diagonal butterfly fish

scorpion fish

black tang

moorish idol

longnose butterfly fish

pinktail triggerfish

Sharks, rays, barracuda, and moray eels are the big predators of the reef, and there are many other predators both small and large. Some have blunt, platelike teeth with which they can crush hard mollusk shells. Others, like the parrot fish, have strong beaklike teeth with which they scrape and graze on living coral and algae. Certain other fish have gill strainers for filtering plankton from the water. Some fish are active swimmers, while others, like the stonefish, move slowly and, hidden by their camouflaged exteriors, lie in wait for their prey. There are fish that burrow and fish that live in dark coral caves and little frogfish that creep about on leglike fins.

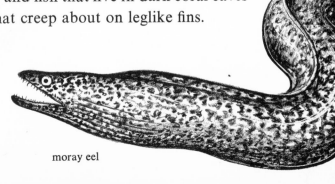

moray eel

In addition to coral, the other animals without backbones are as lovely and as spectacular as the fish and are much more numerous. But unlike the active vertebrates, many of these invertebrates are sessile (attached to some support or stationary) and wait for their food to come to them, either under its own power or borne on currents.

A sea anemone captures a fish

Among the many coral relations are the sea anemones. Purple, pink, yellow, orange, red, green, bright blue, these Anthozoa (flower-animals) look like petaled blossoms in a coral garden. *Stoichactis,* the giant sea anemone, can grow to a foot wide across its base. With it live three small creatures who benefit greatly from this symbiotic association, a small banded reef fish, a crab, and a shrimp. Both the crab and the shrimp are as transparent as glass but are marked with orange spots. These three live in peace and safety among the great anemone's deadly tentacles.

Other coral relations, the gorgonians—including sea

fans, sea plumes, and sea whips—are also animals that appear to be gay and delicate plants. They are supported in the water by a horny material and undulate beautifully with its movements.

The mollusks—snails, clams, oysters, mussels, chitons, slugs, and octopuses—are plentiful and prominent members of the reef community. On the Great Barrier Reef "fossicking," or collecting the rare and beautiful shells of the mollusks which thrive there, is a popular sport although it is hard on the mollusks. The big bailer shell which is used to bail water from canoes, the beautiful cowries, spined spider shells, trochus shells from which come mother-of-pearl, trumpet shells, and cloth-of-gold shells are all considered prize trophies. The white-shelled snail, Nautica, preys upon other mollusks by boring through their shells. Pearl oysters are a valuable resource both for the rare pearls and, much more important commercially, for the mother-of-pearl cut from the shimmering lining of the shell.

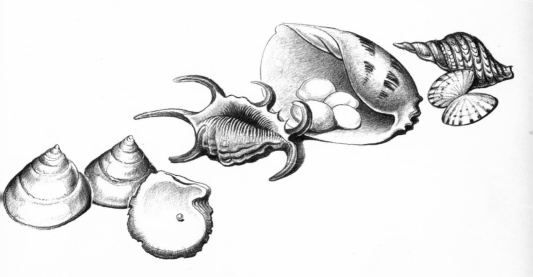

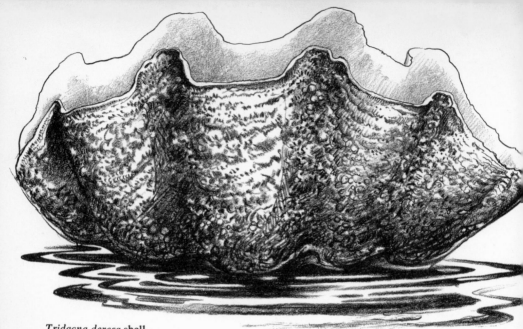

*Tridacna deresa* shell

The "mutton shell," a limpet, is so small that it does not give the protection of an ordinary large shell. But unburdened by the weight of the ordinary limpet-type shell, it can move faster than its relations and does not need the protection. The Conus is the only snail dangerous to man. It has a piercing apparatus that can inject a poison which may temporarily paralyze. The giant clam mentioned earlier, *Tridacna deresa,* has the sinister reputation of sometimes trapping a human swimmer who has accidentally thrust his leg between the heavy shells. *T. deresa* has many *Tridacna* relations that are smaller but still huge, for clams. These are so numerous in some places that they almost seem to litter the reef. Some *Tridacna* clams burrow into the coral as young clams and spend their entire lives within it, enlarging their burrows as they grow. There is also a date mussel which bores into the limestone by dissolving it with an excreted chemical, an acid.

date mussel

The most noticeable sea slugs are the nudibranchs of fantastic shape and equally fantastic color. Nudibranchs are really snails that have evolved to live without their shells, as have our common garden slugs.

gill

"horn"

The sea slug's scientific name, nudibranch, means naked gill

The octopuses are also mollusks that have lost their shells during the course of evolution, and they are quite different from other mollusks in their way of life. Unlike these usually slow, sometimes sessile creatures, octopuses are lively characters and can move swiftly by means of a jet of water produced by the contraction of the muscular mantle. The octopuses are among the most active and intelligent predators of the reef. They live in dark holes and cavelets in the coral and wait for such prey as crabs which they capture with their eight long, sucker-bearing tentacles. To protect themselves from the many that in turn prey on them, they block up the entrance to their caves with bits of coral and reef debris. Octopuses can also eject a dark pigment into the water, creating inky clouds which hide them from octopus predators.

The arthropods (arthropod means "joint-footed") are probably the most widespread and numerous group of animals on the reef or almost any place else, land or sea. There are certainly well over a million species of arthropods in the world and some estimates go even higher. The land literally swarms with insect arthropods. You have only to walk through the long grass of a meadow in late August and see the myriads of grasshoppers that spring out on all sides as you go, butterflies large and small glinting in the sun, and bees working away at almost every blossom of goldenrod and aster, to realize the

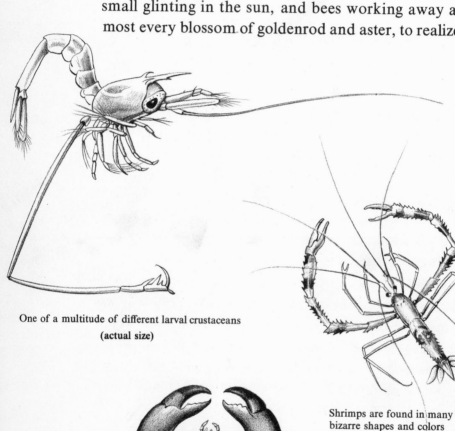

One of a multitude of different larval crustaceans
(actual size)

Shrimps are found in many
bizarre shapes and colors

A coral crab (actual size)

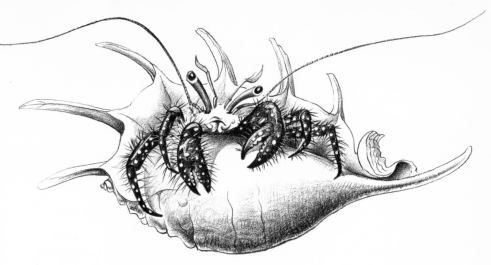

Hermit crabs protect their shell-less abdomens and find safety
by living in empty snail shells. **When they** molt and grow
they must seek a larger house just **the right** size to move into

horde of individuals that each arthropod species includes.
And those you see are only a few; most of the joint-footed
ones are tiny and secretive.

Most marine representatives of the arthropods are
crustaceans: lobsters, crabs, shrimps, many small members of the zooplankton, and their relations. There are
also many crustaceans in fresh water, and a few have
come to the land to live. But the sea swarms with them,
as the land swarms with insects, from minute copepods
of the plankton to monster lobsters weighing forty pounds
or more. The coral reef is rich with swimming, crawling,
creeping, burrowing crustaceans. Some, like barnacles,
have adopted the sessile life. Land crabs, coconut crabs,
and some hermit crabs have evolved to be able to live on
land and inhabit the coral islands.

a copepod

adult (actual size)

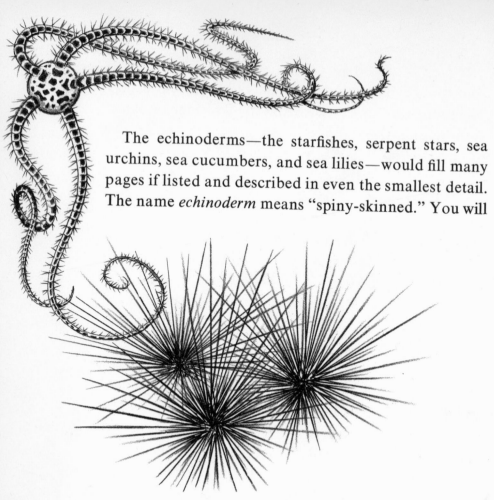

The echinoderms—the starfishes, serpent stars, sea urchins, sea cucumbers, and sea lilies—would fill many pages if listed and described in even the smallest detail. The name *echinoderm* means "spiny-skinned." You will

realize how appropriate the name is if you ever sit on a sea urchin. However, not all echinoderms have long spines or arms. Certain sea cucumbers are rather sausage-shaped, lumpy, and leathery; some, when dried in the sun, become *bêche-de-mer,* valued by the Chinese for food and an article of trade in the South Seas.

Many other invertebrates live in the waters of the reef. Annelid worms, related to our ordinary drab earthworms, seem to have been charmed by the magic of the reef and

transformed into gorgeously colored, plumed beings.
The protozoa—single-celled and small like the "forams"
—radiolarians, and others are important animals to the
reef and swarm in its waters.

Giant sea turtles haul themselves out on the beaches of
coral islands to lay their eggs; and dugongs, large marine
mammals, inhabit many tropic waters. But aside from
fish and men the vertebrates do not form a very important
or influential part in the variety and mass of life in the
waters of the reef. Although we have described only the
smallest fraction of the astronomical number of creatures
that inhabit the coral community, you can now begin to
realize the extent of the swimming, gliding, creeping,
crawling, writhing, spurting, squirting, jet-propelled, drifting, and just plain sitting life—a scene of fantastic but
orderly complexity.

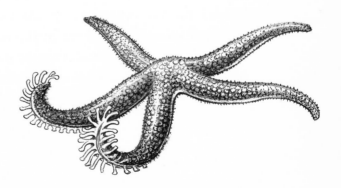

# THE ISLETS OF THE REEF

While the high islands of the Pacific are basically of igneous rock, many are surrounded by fringing or barrier reefs which may have coral islets and which are important to the economy of the island as a whole. They furnish much food for the island people, protect the shores of the main island from the violence of the seas, and affect its ecology in many other ways. But the atoll islets originated from the reef and are of the reef alone.

Some of the reef islets seem to be remnants of coral rock left from the erosion by the sea of a reef that was a little higher than it is at present. This elevated reef is thought to have existed when the sea level was higher during a period of warmer climate that is supposed to have occurred between the present time and the last glacial age, from 2,000 to 5,000 years ago. During this period less water was tied up in the ice of glaciers and the polar ice. However, there are doubts about the occurrence of this higher sea level, and the origin of the rock platforms of the islets is still a question. Whatever their origin, these

54

raised rock platforms have accumulated debris of the reef and coral sand deposited on and about them by currents and storms. Other islets are merely collections of storm-eroded coral fragments, coral sand, and other limy debris on the flat behind the reef's rim. Sometimes this accumulation will be no more than a barren shifting bar. But often the mass has consolidated into limestone by chemical processes, and if enough material has collected for the bar to rise high enough above sea level and absorb fresh water, seeds of wind- and water-borne strand plants sprout and root. These help to hold additional water, anchor the soil with their roots, and enrich it with their remains. These first plants create conditions favorable for more permanent plants and trees which, in turn, add to the island's soil and stability. Both this type of islet and the slightly more substantial rock platform islets then may grow further by the accumulation of more sediment, coral rock fragments, gravel, and sand.

Bushes of scaevola colonize a sand bar

However, they may do just the opposite. Few atoll islets rise over sixteen feet above sea level, and many are lower than this. Their comparatively loose collection of coral rubble and thin soil is subject to the constant erosion by rain and wind and the ever-moving sea. Coral islands are constantly changing shape and size in small ways and in large. Channels are cut through them from sea to lagoon, or existing channels fill and become dry land. Some islets disappear and new ones build. As their seaward side is exposed to the stronger waves and currents of the ocean, and as currents sweeping over the reef from the ocean tend to deposit their load of sediment in the quieter waters on the lagoon side of the islets, the islets may erode on the ocean side, build up on the lagoon side, and move, very slowly of course, inward toward the lagoon or along the reef. Even big reef islands have often been swept by hurricanes or tidal waves, stripped of their plant life, their buildings have been wrecked, and their people drowned or threatened with starvation.

Sometimes atoll islets follow the circumference of the reef in one almost continuous island, like the islands of Fanning and Canton in the central Pacific. Others, like the famous Bikini, have only intermittent islands scattered along the atoll reef. Some lagoons are very small like that of Pulusuk Atoll in the Carolines, which has the appearance of a solid island with a lake in the middle. The number of islets on an atoll varies widely. Ifaluk in the Carolines has only 4, two of which are in-

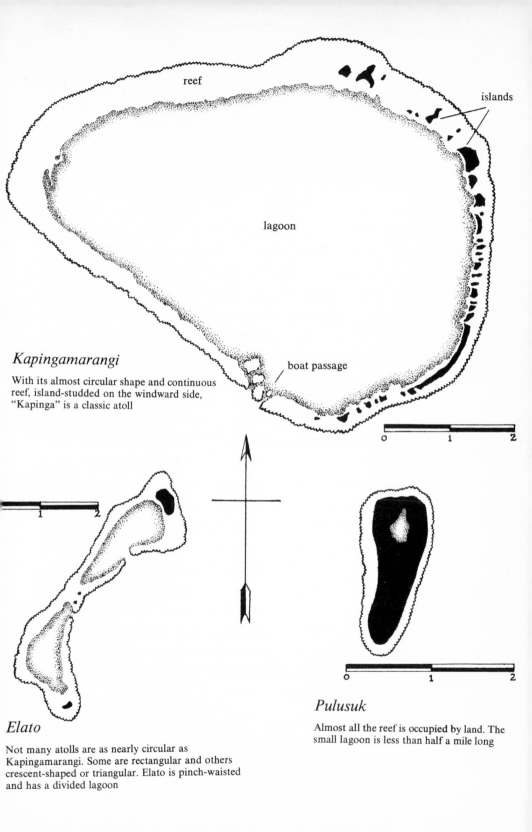

reef

islands

lagoon

### Kapingamarangi

With its almost circular shape and continuous reef, island-studded on the windward side, "Kapinga" is a classic atoll

boat passage

0     1     2

1     2

### Elato

Not many atolls are as nearly circular as Kapingamarangi. Some are rectangular and others crescent-shaped or triangular. Elato is pinch-waisted and has a divided lagoon

### Pulusuk

Almost all the reef is occupied by land. The small lagoon is less than half a mile long

0     1     2

lagoon side           coconut                          breadfruit          taro swamp

*Cross section of atoll islet*

habited, while Kapingamarangi has 33. However, Raroia in the Tuamotus has 280 islets along its reef.

Atolls are quite new features of the world when compared to the age of many other types of islands and the geological features of continents. At Eniwetok, species of Foraminifera in the limestone in the bottom of the drill hole dated back to the Upper Eocene which would make the reef about 50 million years old. The islets, as we know them, doubtless originated much later than this and are not more than a few thousand years old.

Because they are so new, there has not been time on the atoll islets for the establishment of a great variety of plant and animal life such as that found on continents and older islands. This is so particularly on those islands located farthest from large bodies of land. Man arrived on the atolls quite late even in their short history. He brought a large variety of plants and animals with him, either accidentally or deliberately. Until this time all land-living things had to come to an oceanic atoll either by chance in ocean currents; blown by winds; or stuck to the feet, among the feathers, or as seeds in the digestive tracts of birds.

breadfruit    coconut   ocean side

In addition to this severe limit on variety, the opportunities for different ways of living are few on such small low bits of land. Aside from the scarcity of actual space, there are no heights, lowlands, lakes, rivers, wetlands, deserts, forests, or any of the extensive and varied surroundings or the changing altitude and climate such as those which make possible the diversity of life on continents and large islands. We already know that such variety does exist in the waters of the reef. But the dry land of the atoll islets seems barren by contrast and almost opposite to the reef in this respect.

For instance, on the atoll of Raroia, with its 280 islets, it has been calculated that there were only about 30 different plant species before European man arrived. Aside from the island people, there was only one species of mammal, the Pacific island rat, *Rattus exulans,* and 19 species of birds counting both resident and migratory kinds. On Ifaluk Atoll, a team of scientists found but 119 "higher" plants and calculated that only one third of these got there without the help of man. By way of contrast, on the island of Barro Colorado in Gatun Lake in the Panama Canal Zone, 1,057 species of plants alone have been listed.

Originally most plants and animals came to the Pacific islands from the west

A few land birds, some of them peculiar to the islands upon which they are found, live on atolls. As a rule they do not depend greatly on the reef for food and hardly affect the reef community. As with other land organisms, the number and variety of land birds becomes less on the more remote and more easterly islands because most of them have spread eastward from Asia. Some of the small atolls of the mid-Pacific have very few; there are only two species on Raroia, a warbler and the New Zealand cuckoo. The cuckoo is widespread among the atolls and is often the only land bird on coral islands in Polynesia and Micronesia.

However, sea birds are abundant and widely spread. They fish in the waters of the reef and nest on almost all the islands, especially those not inhabited by man or overrun by his constant companion, the rat, or by wild pigs or cats. Sooty terns, for example, nest so thickly on some of the Great Barrier Reef islands that there is scarcely a space not covered by a bird.

Sea birds greatly affect the ecology of the reef and the islands. They prey upon fish and other animals of the reef, and when they die their bodies fall into the sea or on the land and are eaten by other animals or decomposed by bacteria. Most important of all, they concentrate the fertility of the sea as they eat its fish and leave great quantities of droppings to enrich the land where they nest or roost. On the drier atolls where droppings can accumulate, deposits of guano have become so large that they have long been profitably mined for fertilizer. Even on the wetter islands bird droppings are tremendously important to the soil and, consequently, the vegetation. Some of the important producers of guano on coral reef islands are the Laysan and black-footed albatrosses; terns; boobies; frigate, or man-of-war, birds; petrels; and shearwaters.

frigate-bird

Fairy terns lay their eggs and raise their young
on bare branches or rocks

gray-backed

Sooty terns are one of the most common sea birds
of the Pacific. They nest on many of
the islands in incredible numbers

The red-footed booby nests in low bushes

common noddy

250,000 Laysan and black-footed albatrosses breed on Midway Island. This is ⅓ of the world population of these "gooney" birds

Laysan albatross

Fresh ground water is often scarce and sometimes non-existent on atoll islands, especially the smaller ones. One might wonder how there could be any reserves of fresh water at all on such minute bits of land. But falling rain is almost instantly absorbed into porous soil and limestone and, as fresh water is lighter than salt, it is held in the soil and stone literally floating on top of the salt water seeping in from the sea. Since this soil water is not exposed to waves or currents, it mixes very little with the salt although its level rises and falls with the tide in atoll fresh-water wells.

Of course the amount of water also depends upon the amount of rainfall. Over the wide reaches of the Pacific where atolls lie, there is a great deal of difference. The variation spans the entire range from desert to rain-forest conditions. Canton Island in the Phoenix group has but 17 inches of rain per year, while Baker and Howland islands, neighbors to the north, are practically deserts. In the Marshalls the rainfall varies from 157 inches at Jaluit to 53 at Eniwetok. Kapingamarangi in the Carolines to the west has 80 to 100 inches, while Raroia way off to the east has but 46.

fresh water level

fresh ground water

some mixing takes place

Salt water permeates the islet's limestone base

*A fresh-water "lens"*

# MAN AND THE REEF

The history of the peoples who inhabit the atoll islands and other Pacific lands is so complicated, so little known, and so filled with conflicting ideas and theories that a short, simplified account of it is hardly possible. Apparently the islands and Australia have been peopled by a series of emigrations from Southeast Asia in which earlier settlers were often partly or wholly replaced by later ones. For example, the Pygmies of New Guinea and the Negritos of the Philippines are usually considered to be descendants of the earliest settlers of each of these lands. In both places these people have almost entirely been replaced: the Pygmies by Papuans and, later, Papuans by Melanesians in New Guinea; and the Negritos by Indonesians in the Philippines and then the Indonesians by Malays.

The most adventurous and far-ranging of all these shifting peoples were those we now call Polynesians and the inhabitants of Micronesia, almost racially identical. They were among history's finest seamen. Some of their

voyages made those of the fabled vikings seem like pleasure cruises. In their great ocean-going canoes the Polynesians reached far eastward into the wide Pacific to Hawaii, the Marquesas, and even as far as lonely Rapa Nui, or Easter Island. It is quite probable they visited South America where they obtained the sweet potato. These American plants were unknown in Asia but cultivated in Hawaii by 1250.

So it is natural that the Polynesians and Micronesians inhabit most of the atoll islets and high islands that lie long ocean distances from the continental land masses and the large islands. They probably are as mixed a people as Europeans. Aside from a beautiful golden-brown skin they look a good deal like Europeans and are considered to have had ancient origins in common. In general they are tall, handsome, and graceful. The beauty

of their women is the stuff of song and legend. Their
original way of life was easygoing and free from much of
the strife and restricting customs of more highly developed civilizations. Their physical environment was the
gemlike atolls or the startling mountainous grandeur of
the high islands. All this has created an atmosphere of

romance that has given rise to the South Seas Island Legend—a fable of Eden-like isles of peace, repose, and love.

Of course, the life on the islands was never Eden-like. There were wars, disease, storms, hunger, all the tragedy that seems to be part of the human lot everywhere. Life on many of the atoll islands was often miserable. But whatever life was really like, before the Europeans came to the Pacific it was quite different from what it is today. Whether or not it was a better life is hard to judge. In pre-European days man was an integral part of the reef community. He existed entirely on the resources about him without need of or reference to the rest of the world.

Man played several parts in the complex community of reef and islet. On the reef he was a large and hungry predator. Unlike most animals, he preyed upon a wide range of organisms from sea cucumbers and clams to tuna fish. On the islets he was both a vegetarian and a predator. He ate or otherwise used many of the plants and hunted the sea birds and turtles and their eggs and land crustaceans. He affected the islets especially as he dug in their soils, buried his dead, altered their vegetation both by use and by importing and spreading new kinds of plants and animals.

In turn the atolls affected man as he adjusted his ways to this strict and relatively poor environment. Almost all the island skills were those permitting the greatest possible yield of the materials of life. Even the island religions were part of this existence. They contained many taboos

*Spearfishing on the rim of the reef*

such as the prohibition of eating certain birds or other articles of food at certain times. Many of these taboos were such that valuable resources were conserved and not exhausted.

In this remarkable economy two trees were of great importance, the pandanus and the coconut. Before the days of trade the pandanus was as important as the famous coconut and perhaps more so. Its stiltlike roots support it in shifting soils or mud. Its nutlike fruit was a valuable food and its leaves furnished baskets, mats, sails, and thatch for roofs. It can exist on islands with little or no fresh ground water and its seeds can stay alive after long soaking in salt water.

The coconut can also grow well on islets with no fresh ground water, although it does better on the wetter islands. Its remarkable dense root system can soak up quantities of water like a sponge. However, its nut cannot

The pandanus' stiltlike prop roots support it in shifting sands or swampy soil, its dried leaves are material for baskets, mats, and thatch, and its fruit is a nourishing food

The ability of the coconut palm to grow in unfavorable places is shown by these trees on an islet which is little more than a sand bar

stand salt water for nearly as long a time as can the pandanus seed. The distribution of coconuts throughout the islands was probably mainly due to man. From the coconut the people of the reefs got food and drink, household utensils, lumber for boats and houses, thatch, and rope.

The breadfruit tree does not stand salty soil water as well as the pandanus and the coconut and needs a comparatively fertile soil. However, breadfruit was another very important plant and was the main source of starchy food, or "bread," on many atolls. The fruit was baked or boiled. Breadfruit was especially important as it was the only food which could be stored for any length of time. The pulp was soaked, kneaded, wrapped in leaves, and buried in the ground. Here it fermented in a way similar to sauerkraut and would keep for years. This reserve often meant the difference between starvation and life to the people of an atoll when a hurricane had destroyed all other crops.

Big breadfruit trees have trunks as much as 6 feet in diameter and reach 90 to 100 feet in height. The yellow-green fruits are as big as melons

Puraka is a local Micronesian name for a plant related to taro.
It provides a better crop on atolls than does taro.
Like taro its roots are usually mashed or grated,
kneaded into doughy balls, and cooked

Taro and puraka also were other sources of starchy food. But they are plants difficult to grow on atoll islets because they need moist soil. Artificial swamps were often made by digging pits deep enough to become damp with ground-water seepage. The pits were then filled with vegetable matter which rotted and formed a mucky, swampy soil. The taro pits ranged in size from small holes to gardens of several acres. These large pits must have taken a tremendous amount of work, particularly without any modern tools even as simple as a steel shovel.

There were other vegetable foods such as arrowroot, bananas, sweet potatoes, and possibly a few others grown on some atoll islets before Europeans arrived in the Pacific. So the vegetable diet was really meager and monotonous. But the edible products of the sea and reef were as bountiful as the products of the land were skimpy. Apparently pigs, dogs, and chickens were not raised to any great extent, if at all, on the atolls in pre-European days. There would have been little food to spare for them.

So, aside from birds and their eggs, coconut and land crabs, all the meat in an atoll diet came from the sea, supplied by fish and other marine animals. Plentiful lobsters, edible crabs and other crustaceans, hundreds of species of fish and many mollusks, plus turtles and turtle eggs on some atolls, and many other invertebrates were more or less easily obtained.

Because of this dependence on food from the sea and the reef the Polynesians and Micronesians were almost as much at ease in the water as they were upon the land. In addition to their abilities as sailors in their great long-distance canoes, they used smaller dugouts in home waters with equal skill. They caught fish with spear, net, hook, trap, and by hand and, hundreds of years before the development of skin diving, they were swimmers and divers without peer and could almost equal this modern form without any equipment at all.

Since the time when Europeans first came to the Pacific much has happened to change this simple way of life. Unscrupulous and irresponsible seamen, adven-

turers, and traders easily took advantage of people inno-
cent of foreign ways. Overly strict and sometimes fanatical
missionaries often "converted" entire islands, forcing the
inhabitants to change their way of life and their beliefs
too quickly and too much. Often their own traditions were
destroyed, and little was left to take their place. Imperial-
istic nations took over islands and often exploited them
without much regard for the rights or well-being of the inhabitants. Tuberculosis and other strange diseases to
which the islanders had no resistance decimated many
populations. It is said that when Europeans arrived, the
Polynesians numbered a million people. By 1900 four
fifths of this number had disappeared. Many lost their
will to live under these conditions, and the people of

Trapping fish in shallow water with rope entwined with coconut leaves

whole islands seemed sometimes to be dying off slowly for no material reason at all.

Today great airplanes make almost nothing of the vast sea distances of the Pacific over which the old-time Polynesian sailors struggled. Manufactured products of industrial nations flood island markets. The shadow of World War II, which changed much on the reefs and islands, was lifted from the Pacific world only a few years past. More recently, test nuclear bombs have exploded over beautiful atolls like Bikini and Eniwetok and Christmas Island. The ancient way of life has either already been, or soon will be, entirely changed everywhere. On many islands the people are now almost completely dependent on imported products. Many of the old skills of fishing, food-

gathering and preparation, gardening, canoe-building, as well as knowledge of the surroundings, are gone and forgotten. The people of an atoll would find it hard or impossible to exist if imports were cut off. Such crops as taro are no longer grown on many atolls. Outside products like soft drinks, radios, tinned meat, flour and other grains, tools, and outboard motors, which were almost unthinkable luxuries a few years ago, have become necessities today.

In this new economy the coconut palm has greatly increased in importance. From it comes copra, the name given to the dried meat of the nut, which is about the only cash crop or export of the atolls. Vegetable oils extracted from copra are used to make margarine, soap, and other products. There are good world markets for copra today, but if these should ever fail, the result would be disastrous to an economy based on this one product. The atoll people would either have to be subsidized from outside or starve. It would be very hard for them to go back to the old ways so long forgotten. It has been said that in many places the old skills would have to be taught to the people by anthropologists who have studied the ancient way of life.

There are no mineral resources in the atolls. The distribution of guano is limited to a few islands. In spite of its bounty for native inhabitants, the sea does not provide much that can be used for export. Most fish are small and the atolls are far away from any large market. Even if the fish could be marketed, the added use would

probably exhaust their numbers. The demand for *bêche de mer* is as limited as are its supplies. Mother-of-pearl is a doubtful product in these days of plastics. Also the taking of oyster and trochus shell must be carefully limited in order to conserve these mollusks and keep them from becoming extinct. The pearl itself is now really only a by-product of the shell industry and has no great importance economically in spite of the tremendous value of some individual pearls. Handicrafts are important only on islands where the quality of workmanship is high. On Kapingamarangi, for example, the sale of pandanus mats, coconut graters, and the like is an important source of income. Perhaps the rapidly expanding tourist trade will be of economic help on some atolls as it is now on high islands.

Actually atolls do not produce any product of great importance to world trade or industry. But they are able to support a small human population at a moderate standard of living. As the customs and products of industrial civilization become more and more important to the island people, their original workable economy and customs become more disrupted and life, although easier physically, becomes more difficult in other ways. It is hard to change from a life which fits a world of sea and reef and tiny island—a world where wind and storm and fish, taro, coconut, and pandanus were the important things—to a life adjusted to radios, jet planes, mechanized wars and atom bombs, commerce and tin cans and, perhaps hardest of all, strange ways of life and new values. It is the responsibility of the large nations who hold power and influence in the Pacific to find ways to make existence as fulfilling as possible for the island people and to try to heal the wounds of the past.

Today scientists, geologists, biologists, anthropologists, and others work in teams to study the reefs and their people not only to find knowledge to make the future brighter for island people, but for the benefit of all men. Today things are brighter. The scattered islanders are helped to make the most of their meager environment, and medicine is checking or curing disease. Island people are healthier, mentally and physically, in many places than they have been for years. Populations are increasing again. Of course, increasing population will bring new problems. Pressures on limited atoll resources will be greater than ever before under the new island economy, and strict conservation will have to be observed. For instance, with every export of copra, some part of the plant foods of the island soil in which it grew are also exported. This fertility will have to be replaced if the none-too-rich soil is not to be exhausted.

In spite of the promise of the future, enough time and money are not yet being devoted to such work in a world where missiles and rockets and getting to the moon ahead of some other nation seem to be the only important things. Space flight *is* important. But the unhappy condition of earth, our own planet, proves that we make it too important. It seems wrong that we must pay so much attention to outer space when we have not yet learned to use the space we have on earth as well as it should be used.

We see in the lonely atoll and its unsubstantial islets and its ring of crashing surf from the trade-wind-driven, mid-Pacific swell, not only a pretty sight, an ocean jewel, but a whole world of life from diatoms of the plankton and fragile coral polyps, through a galaxy of form and habit to man and his urgent troubles. And all this from a combination of a few groups of the simpler forms of life, the warm and fertile tropic ocean, and the radiant energy of the blazing sun. Perhaps we can best sum up this wonder of burgeoning life in the words of Charles Darwin who wrote in chapter 20 of *The Voyage of the Beagle:*

"It is impossible to behold these waves [ocean breakers] without feeling a conviction that an island though built of the hardest rock, let it be porphyry, granite, or quartz, would ultimately yield and be demolished by such an irresistible power. Yet these low, insignificant coral islets stand and are victorious: for here another power, as an antagonist, takes part in the contest. The organic forces [the forces of life] separate the atoms of carbonate of lime, one by one, from the foaming breakers, and unite them into a symmetrical structure. Let the hurricane tear up its thousand huge fragments; yet what will that tell against the accumulated labor of myriads of architects at work night and day, month after month? Thus do we see the soft and gelatinous body of the polypus [polyp], through the agency of vital laws, conquering the great mechanical power of the waves of an ocean which neither the art of man nor the inanimate works of nature could successfully resist."

# Index

*INDICATES ILLUSTRATION